Hägar in a Fix

by Dik Browne

ATTICA
PUBLICATIONS

Introducing . . .

HÄGAR THE HORRIBLE a hard-working Barbarian businessman. He's in sacking and looting.

His wife, HELGA. She finds civilising Hägar a 24-hour-a-day job!

This is HAMLET, their son, a real problem child! He insists on wearing his hair short, bathing, reading and otherwise behaving in a very unbarbarian manner.

HONI, their daughter, is sixteen years old, and still not married!

But that's not the end of Hägars troubles . . . there's also LUCKY EDDIE who must be the most hopeless assistant in history!

Attica Publications, an imprint of Argus Communications Ltd., DLM House, Edinburgh Way, Harlow, Essex CM20 2HL, England.

ISBN 1 85176 069 5

Printed and bound in Great Britain by Cox & Wyman Ltd, Reading

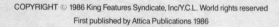

Look out for these forthcoming new exciting Hagar products in your local giftshops and bookshops.

● Albums ● More Cartoon Books ●
● Wall Calendars ●
● Reminder Calendars ● Diaries ●
● Greeting Cards for all Occasions ●
● Postcards ● Posters ● Stick-Em-Ups ●
● Gift Wrap ● Gift Tags ●

© 1986 King Features Syndicate, Inc.
World Rights Reserved.

For more details contact:
Argus Communications Ltd.,
DLM House, Edinburgh Way, Harlow, Essex, CM20 2HL.
Tel: (0279) 39441.